Swimming to

Swimming to Fitness

by

Carol Hicks

THORSONS PUBLISHING GROUP

First published in 1988

© Carol Hicks 1989

British Library Cataloguing in
Publication Data

Hicks, Carol
    Swimming to fitness.
    1. Swimming — Manuals
    I. Title
    797.2'1

    ISBN 0-7225-1794-7

*Published by Thorsons Publishers
Limited, Wellingborough,
Northamptonshire, NN8 2RQ,
England*

Printed in Great Britain by
Woolnough Bookbinding Limited,
Irthlingborough, Northamptonshire

Typeset by Harper Phototypesetters
Limited, Northampton

10   9   8   7   6   5   4   3   2   1

Dedication

To my husband David for his patience and advice whilst I was compiling this book

Acknowledgements

I would like to thank Professor J. M. Cameron MD, PhD (Glas), DMJ — Medical Advisor to the Amateur Swimming Association and Alice Coyle SRN, SCM — an Independent Midwife.

Contents

Welcome to the water!

Swimming is without question the best all-round exercise for fitness as it embraces and makes use of every muscle group in the body. The heart and lungs are worked properly (the cardiovascular system) and blood circulation is increased and improved as the muscles are exercised and toned up. Swimming is also exercise through enjoyment — unlike a lot of land work which can be very tedious. Nor is there any great expense involved in swimming regularly: costume, towel and perhaps a pair of goggles will last a long time and most public pools are not expensive to enter and enjoy.

You do not have to be a good swimmer to benefit from the swimming programmes described in this book. Whatever your level of swimming ability you will find here advice to help you improve your level of fitness — and also your swimming — to enable you to tackle some of the more advanced suggestions at the end of the book. A lot depends on how fit you are, or want to be. You can exercise in water just enough to keep you out of the doctor's surgery, or go much further to the extent of competing in a Masters' Swimming Programme with a local club. Lots of adults find that being involved with a club helps to motivate them — and many are quite good at it even though they had no great success in swimming in earlier years.

In trying to regain fitness after illness or injury, a swimming programme really comes into its own: water therapy is invaluable because the body is working against the passive resistance offered by the water. Swimming is particularly beneficial in the treatment of muscle injuries and respiratory problems and we'll be looking too at swimming's relevance to women during pregnancy and, later, in getting back into shape.

Dictionaries define fitness as 'the state of being fit', but what is 'fit'? What does it mean to be 'fit'? Being fit is feeling relaxed and happy with oneself mentally and physically. Getting there involves improving the body's strength, stamina and flexibility. There is no better way to gain in health and wellbeing than to swim for fitness and, with the aid of this book, we can do that together!

Starting your fitness programme

Starting any fitness programme should be looked upon as fun and not as tedium. Later on, it may become more serious, as you acquire a higher state of fitness, but that depends on what you want from this applied effort. If in any doubt about a medical problem or recovering from illness, it goes without saying, that a doctor's advice must be sought. Once you have the all clear, start slowly and build up as you progress. It might be a good idea to start with a single session a week, then increase the number of sessions as fitness improves.

Maybe twenty to thirty minutes will be sufficient on each occasion for the first few weeks, gradually building up to an hour or more or, preferably, increasing the number of sessions. No acute discomfort should be felt either during the work out or afterwards. You should come away with a feeling of wellbeing, although tired.

As a build up, prior to starting your swim fitness programme in earnest, try visiting the local swimming pool and doing a little more than you would normally do in a recreational swim session. After a short warm up, continue with bursts of fast swimming, lasting no more than 15 seconds or so. Rest again, then repeat this twice more. Follow this with a nice leisurely swim down, then out of the water, a relaxing hot shower and a rub down with a luxurious towel will make you feel better — and fitter — already. Once your body has started waking up to this routine, you can increase the distance covered and the intensity, leading to a set schedule of work, tailor-made to your own strokes and circumstances. How to do this is explained on p 43.

Warm up

Before any sort of exercise begins, a warm up is essential. This is used to prevent any muscle injury and to prepare your heart and lungs for a work load over and above your normal daily routine. This warm up can be done in the water or alternatively on dry land, well away from the poolside. Many modern swimming pools are part of sports complexes with halls and exercise areas ideal for this purpose. The more basic the warm up pattern, the better. Ideally, wear a tracksuit over your swimming costume and once warmed up on land with the following routine, get straight into the water.

The land warm up should start with thirty seconds of gentle running or jogging on the spot, then ten tuck jumps. Alternate between running and jumping for three to four minutes, building up the pace as the blood begins to flow. This simple exercise will raise the pulse count quite rapidly, particularly if you put some effort into it.

Warm up: jogging on the spot

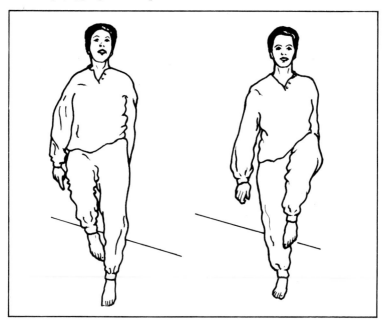

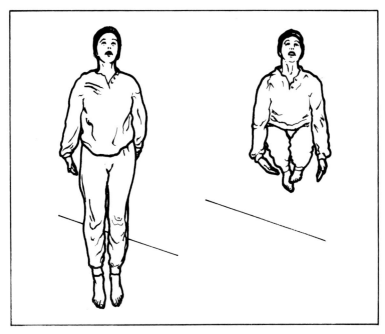

Above *Warm up: tuck jumps*

Below *Stretching: head and neck rolling*

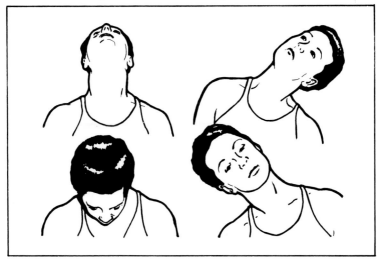

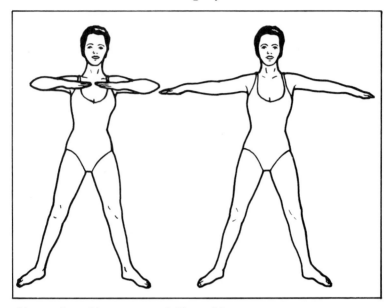

Above *Stretching: press and fling with arms*

Below *Stretching: arm circles*

Above *Stretching: trunk bending*

Below *Stretching: high kicks*

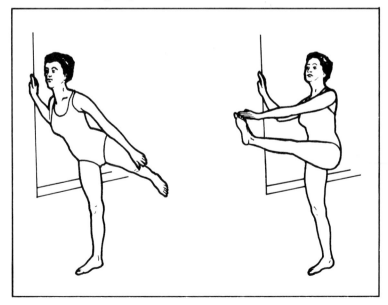

Stretching and flexibility exercises should follow, allowing you to get your breath back. Run right through the range of movements, starting with head and neck rolling, first one way and then the other. Move on to the upper arms and shoulders, doing 'press and fling' with the arms, keeping the elbows in line with the shoulders. Continue by doing large circles with the arms, pressing against the joints and thus getting the full range of movement. Trunk bending from side to side and in circles will also help to improve mobility and suppleness. Try also some high kicks with each leg in turn to release the hamstrings, followed by half and full squats for strength and endurance.

Ankle rotation is a must to finish on. Without flexible ankles your swimming will suffer badly. This dry land warm up and flexibility session will take only ten minutes or so, but it is guaranteed to improve your swimming and thus your fitness.

A warm up in water should start with a slow swim using exaggerated movements, ending with much quicker stroking to raise the pulse rate. Normal strokes used for warm up would be front and back crawl. Breast stroke should be avoided in the early part of warm up, as the knees are placed under too much strain due to the pressure of water on the backward kick. The distance covered in the water on warm up varies with each swimmer. A distance swimmer generally needs a lot more time warming up than a sprinter. Once you fall into the habit you will find your optimum warm up time on land and/or in the water.

Trying to obtain fitness through swimming activities means

Stretching: ankle rotation

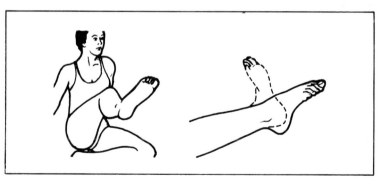

that you have to swim further and put more effort into your strokes than in normal recreational swimming. This means that your swimming strokes should be reasonably good technically to enable you to achieve longer distances and fully exercise all muscle groups. Although this book is not intended as a guide to better swimming, but to help you attain a better state of fitness, there are many factors which make it desirable to try to improve your strokes. Most important of these is that a good stroke will use less effort and take you further. It also looks good to see a swimmer going smoothly through the water, *using* the water and not *fighting* it.

Psychologically, better stroking makes you feel confident too. Let us then run through all the recognized swimming strokes briefly, to make sure we are on the right lines. The most popular stroke used by fitness swimmers is the front crawl stroke, so we will start with that.

Front crawl

The body position for this, the fastest of all strokes, is as flat as possible in a prone position, stretched out just under the surface of the water. The head should be in a natural position, with the eyes looking forward and downward and the water line should cut between the hair line and the eyebrows.

Front crawl: position of head

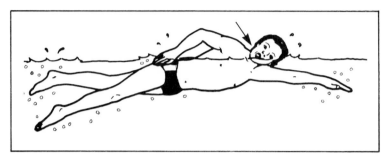

Front crawl: breathing

Breathing

The body should roll in a longitudinal axis for breathing, without moving sideways or laterally. Breathing will then take place to the side, without it being necessary to lift the head to the front. Try and breathe as low as possible to the water line, keeping your head steady. Explosive breathing, that is a quick puff out, then in, is more desirable than trickle breathing (where the air is gently exhaled underwater before the head is turned and a breath is taken).

Leg action

The legs work fairly closely together, alternating, just like a walking action but in a horizontal position. The depth of the

Front crawl: leg action

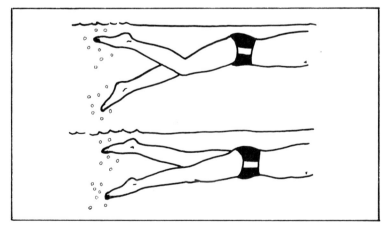

kick will vary from 12 to 18 in, but it is important that the toes should be 'planter flexed', that is, pushed away from your shins. This is where the flexibility of the ankles comes in. Not a lot of propulsion comes from the leg action, but the legs act as a stabilizing agent for the body whilst the arms are pulling. All movement of the legs should start from the hips and not at the knees.

Arm action

As in most swimming strokes, the arms are the main agents of propulsion. Working in time with the legs in an alternating action, one arm pulls through the water, whilst the other recovers over the water. The hand enters the water in front of the shoulders and sinks to a catch position, 6 to 8 in under the water. Downward and backward pressure is applied along the side, and just under the body. The elbow should be kept high at this point to get maximum pressure on the water, with the hand facing

Right *Front crawl: hand/arm action: entry*

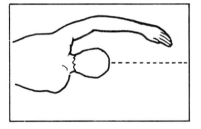

Below *Front crawl: hand/arm action: catch*

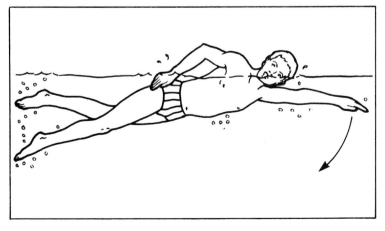

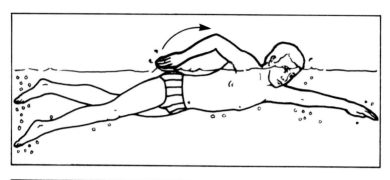

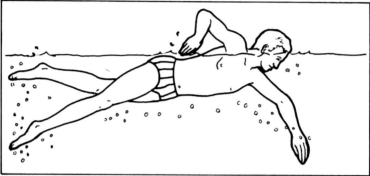

Top and Above *Front crawl: pull*

Below *Front crawl: push*

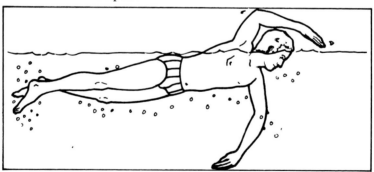

backwards. The elbow bends to about 90° under the chest then the hand continues to a stretch position with the hand just touching the thigh. The body rolls to about 35° allowing breathing to take place just as the hand that finishes the push

Front crawl: elbow shape   *Front crawl: arm recovery*

is about to leave the water. The elbow raises out of the water first and recovers over the water as smoothly and quickly as possible, ready to enter once more.

The front crawl stroke, in fact, is similar to walking: a two leg beat action is used to one complete arm cycle (then one arm pulls whilst the opposite leg kicks downwards). Sprinters, however, normally use a six leg beat to arm cycle ratio to raise the body higher out of the water and to get more propulsion, but the energy used is very costly.

Back stroke

The body position this time is supine, lying as flat as possible in the water with the head back, eyes looking upward and slightly

Back stroke: lying position

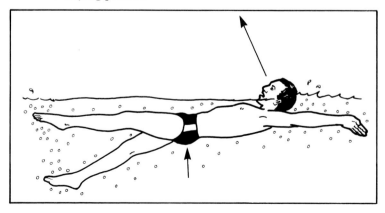

forward. The hips should be kept nice and high and certainly not dropped, allowing for good progress through the water with less resistance to forward motion.

Leg action

The leg kick, as with front crawl is initiated from the hips and not the knees, with the toes stretched and the legs kept fairly straight. Most of the pressure is on the up kick unlike front crawl where the pressure is on the downward kick. Once again, flexibility in the ankles is most important to ensure propulsion is obtained from the instep of the foot. In fact people with no extension of the foot suffer a retardation to progress and not forward movement! An alternating kick is used just like front crawl. Six leg beats per complete arm cycle is normal for back

Back stroke: leg action

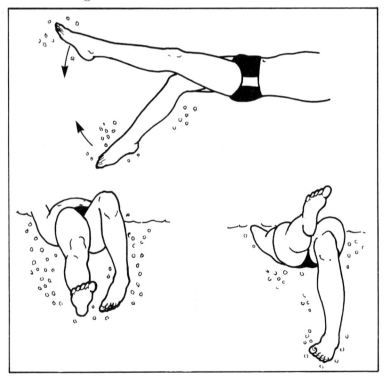

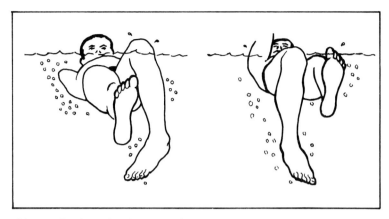

Above *Back stroke: foot extension*

Below *Back stroke: arm and ear*

crawl, such is the importance of the kick in stabilizing the body position.

Arm action

We look at the arms in swimming as the oars because this is where propulsion is generated. Lying on our backs, it is impossible to see where the hand is entering the water. The

Left *Back stroke: arm recovery*

Below *Back stroke: hand leaving the water*

important thing is to ensure that the upper arm is brushing against the ear on that side with the arm straight. Unless we have extremely big ears this will ensure that the hand is entering the water between the head and the shoulder height, with little finger leading. The hand sinks again to 8 in or so under the water, when we start our pulling action. The hand should face the direction of pull, that is towards your feet, keeping your elbow as high in the stroke as possible. During this pulling phase when the hand is in line with the shoulder the arm should be bent at the elbow to about 90°. At this stage the hand is at the highest point in the propulsive phase. The hand continues the backward push until fully extended below the thigh. The hand leaves the water thumb first and as the arm recovers over the water the rotation takes place allowing the little finger to enter the water once more. One arm pulls while the other recovers to begin the next stroke. Breathing creates no problems as the mouth is clear above the water, but a regular pattern should be used. Breathe in on one arm and breathe out on the other.

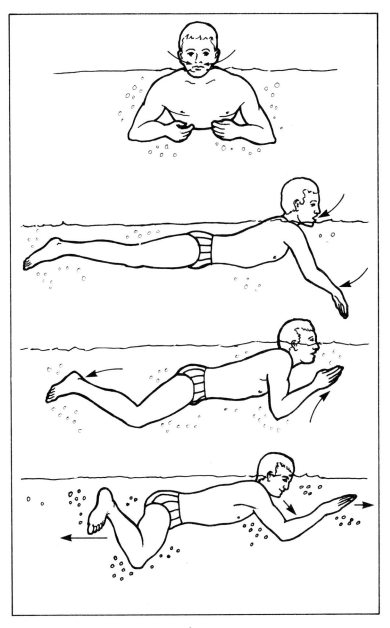

This page *Breast stroke: general*

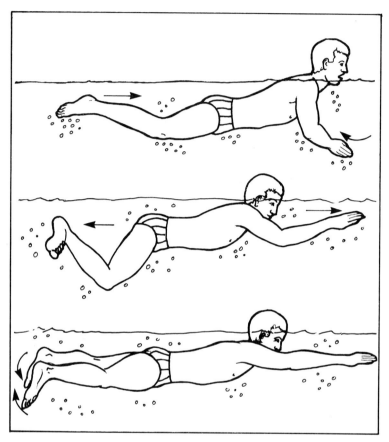

Breast stroke: general

Breast stroke

Breast stroke is often favoured by adult swimmers and women in particular, as breathing creates no problems and you can see where you are going. Survival swimming relies on breast stroke, likewise life-saving and recreational swimming. For whatever reasons we swim breast stroke, the action of arms and legs must be simultaneous and in the same horizontal plane to be most effective (no alternating movements are allowed as in the crawl strokes).

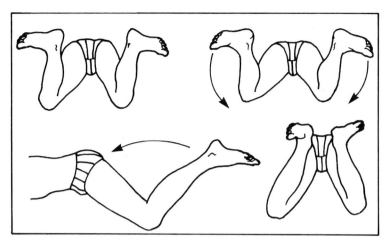

Breast stroke: leg action — whip kick

Leg action

During the leg action, the kick backwards must be made with the feet turned outward, the body must be kept perfectly on the breast, with shoulders in line with the water surface. The

Breast stroke: leg action — wedge kick
a) knees draw up and out
b) feet extend out to wedge shape

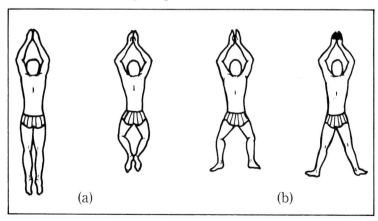

(a)   (b)

body position in this stroke is slightly slanted due to the fact that when the legs recover they must remain in the water. The head is held so that the eyes look over the surface of the water. The leg kick creates more propulsion than other strokes, with some female competitive swimmers getting more propulsion from the leg kick than the arm action. The amount of propulsion gained will depend on the strength of the leg muscles and the mobility of the ankle, knee and hip joints.

There are two types of leg action used in the breast stroke. First, there is the whip kick, a quick direct kick used by competitive swimmers and then there is the wedge kick, a slow wide kick with no direct force backwards, mostly used by recreational swimmers. We shall concentrate on the whip kick, which gives greater speed by increasing the stroke rate. From the legs extended position, the heels are drawn up towards the bottom, about hip width apart. The legs draw up to the body at an angle of approximately 120° to 130°. At this point the feet turn out into a 'dorsi flex' position to begin the outward and backward thrust. The insides of the feet, the ankles and the lower legs are now in a good position to drive vigorously against the water. The kick begins by pushing the feet against the water with the heels leading in a curved pathway, finishing as the feet are brought together with a swirl. A lot of propulsion is created by this whip action.

Breast stroke: 'dorsi flex' position of feet

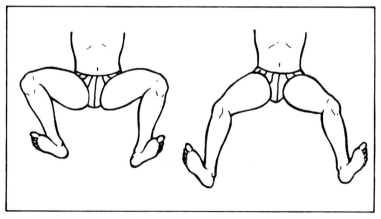

Arm action

The arm action is a continuous circling movement, with only a short glide at the end of the stroke. The type of arm action that goes with the whip kick is the bent arm pull, which begins with the arms fully extended in front of the body, hands touching. At the beginning of the pull the hands should be 6 to 8 in under the surface in a catch position. The hands turn slightly outwards and downwards during the first part of the pull, with the elbows straight. When the hands are moved out just past the elbows, the elbows bend and the hands start coming together, just under

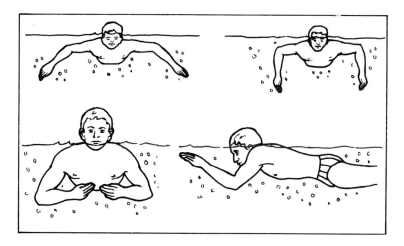

Above *Breast stroke: arm action*
a) catch position
b) pull
c) hands together under chest

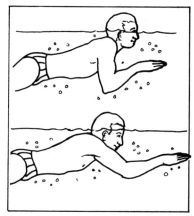

Right *Breast stroke: hands move forward to stretch position*

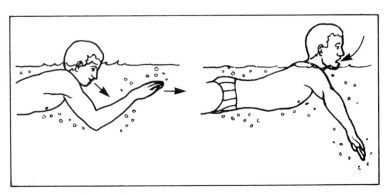

Breast stroke: breathing

the chest. This should be an accelerating action creating lots of propulsion. From here the hands move forward to the stretch position once again. Breathing should take place at the end of the propulsive phase, with a short, sharp explosive movement.

The timing of breast stroke is very important. Use a rhythm of *pull, breathe, kick,* and keep all movements smooth and unhurried.

Butterfly stroke

Butterfly stroke is the newest recognized competitive stroke, but because of its comparative difficulty is rarely used by the 'fitness' swimmer. Before the stroke was recognized in 1952, breast stroke used to be swum with an over-the-water arm recovery. Most swimmers then used a breast stroke leg kick

Butterfly: breast stroke legs and fly arms

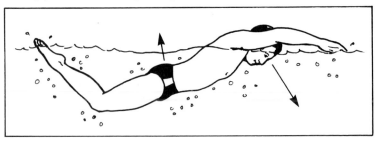

and butterfly arms, but now a dolphin leg action is used, because this has a faster turnover. The body position in dolphin butterfly swimming is as flat as possible to minimize resistance. Undulation of the body is unavoidable, but should be kept to a minimum.

Leg action

We start the leg action with the legs extended about 20 to 24 in at the end of the down kick. The up thrust starts with the legs being raised, still extended, and the soles of the feet creating

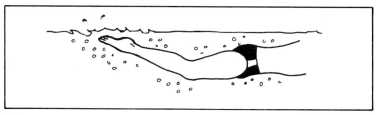

Above *Butterfly: dolphin legs*

Below *Butterfly: knees bent to 90°, fully extended ankles*

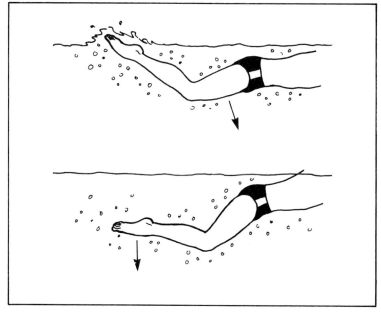

an upward and backward force on the water. The hips will now start to drop, leading the upper leg in a downwards movement with the knees bending whilst the lower leg and feet continue to rise. This action continues until the knees bend to about 90° and the ankles are fully extended. The lower legs then start the propulsive thrust downwards and as they continue to thrust deeper the hips will start to rise. The legs continue the downward movement until fully extended, ready to start the cycle once again. Both legs must move simultaneously, up and down, balancing the movement of the upper body.

Arm action

The arm action is the major source of propulsion in a stroke where strength and mobility of the shoulders are most important. The arms move simultaneously and continuously. Entry of the hands should be in front of, or just outside, the shoulder line.

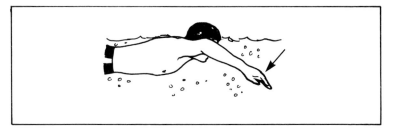

Butterfly: hands in catch position

The hands go into the catch position, that is 6 to 8 in under the water, as early as possible, with the hands fixing on the water, facing the direction of pull. From here the hands pull downwards, backwards and sideways. The arms bend when the hands are 12 to 18 in deep and the hands move towards each other in a curved pathway just under the chest. The hands continue the push phase, right through to the thighs ready to start the recovery.

The hands will leave the water first on recovery, palms facing upwards and breathing takes place by hyper-extending the neck to allow the chin to make a furrow in the water. On recovery (the arms coming out of the water) the hands are carried forward in a flinging action ready to enter the water again. By the time

Above *Butterfly: hands curved pathway under the chest*
a) actual
b) diagrammatical

Below *Butterfly: hands leaving water on recovery*

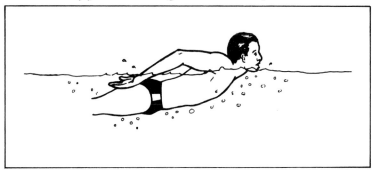

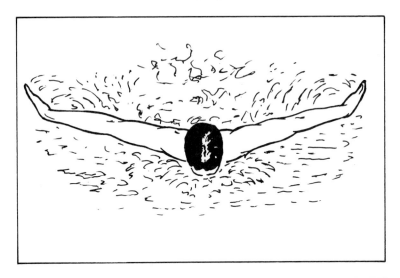

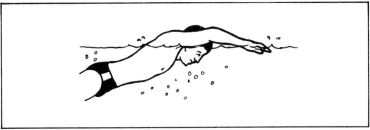

Top *Butterfly: arms in flinging action*

Above *Butterfly: hands enter in front of shoulders*

Below *Butterfly: second, less vigorous kick during breathing*

the hands are passing the shoulder line, breathing should have finished, so that the head drops back in the water and the hands enter in front of the shoulders ready to start again.

Most butterfly swimmers have a regular pattern of breathing, usually once every two strokes. This makes for less interference with the stroke. It is normal to use two leg kicks per arm cycle. The first and major leg kick normally takes place just as the hands are in the catch position at the start of the pull. The second and less vigorous kick is when the hands are just leaving the water on recovery and as breathing takes place. The more you practise dolphin butterfly stroke, the better. What a challenge to master this most prestigious of strokes and how fit it will make you.

We have now looked at the main competitive strokes and one of these strokes will be your favourite, but variation is the key to interest. Try all the strokes at one time or another and see how easily you pick up new ideas.

Incentives to keep you going

We need incentives, even at this early stage of our swim fitness programme, so we need some evidence of improvement. Progress can be measured in a number of ways.

1) By timing your strokes over 25 metres and looking for faster times, but maintaining a good stroke.
2) By taking a pulse count over 15 seconds then multiplying by 4 to give a count over one minute.

The real test of fitness by pulse rate, however, is not how high the count is, but how fast it recovers.

The first assessment of fitness by faster swims is pretty obvious, as one can see by the clock whether your time is improving or not. The second, by way of pulse reading, is slightly more difficult as a pace clock is needed if you are in the water. Use two fingers over a pressure point and count over a 15 second

Pulse taking: two fingers over wrist

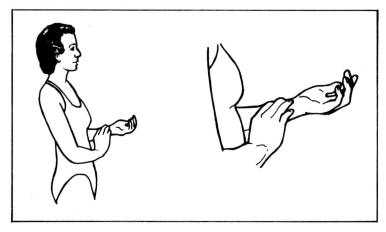

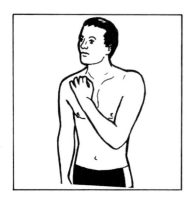

Pulse taking: sub-clavian artery

period. The most commonly used pressure point in swimming is the carotid artery just under and to the side of the chin, towards the ear. The other is the sub-clavian artery just under the clavical bone, as illustrated.

To see how quickly your pulse rate recovers, take your pulse again after one minute and log the result. See how quickly your pulse returns to its resting rate taken before you began. This will provide another positive way of seeing your fitness programme improving. Remember to keep a record of your pulse counts and also the best times taken for your swims.

After a good swimming session reward yourself with a small (non-fattening!) treat.

Scheduling your swimming programme

For our first official schedule, we will use distances of no more than 100 metres to 400 metres for the initial stages. Gentle swims with good stroke work are preferable at this stage. As a regular pattern of swimming within a session is established, stick to it, and with improvements in fitness increase the number of sessions and up rate your work outs. We call these swimming fitness sessions 'schedules', so we shall use this term from here on.

Let us now look at some basic swimming schedules to set us on our way. A gradual build up is more sensible and more beneficial in the long term.

Assuming that you can swim, though you are not perhaps a strong swimmer, we need to do a little stretching on the side of the pool to limber up (see the warm up p 16). Once we enter the water our warm up continues (Schedule 1, part 1), and our schedule will read like this:

Schedule 1
1) A 200 metres slow swim (warm up) with a bit more effort towards the end to increase the heart rate.
2) Swim your favourite stroke at a steady pace for about 5 minutes, trying to improve the technique.
3) 4 × 100 metre swim using two strokes if possible, alternating the strokes each 100 metres, then a rest for 60 seconds and repeat.
4) Just easy swimming to warm down and relax.

This type of schedule could last for up to three weeks or more, depending on how many times you visit the pool. In a short while, you will find that your body is adapting to this work load and that the schedule is not taxing enough. This is the time to

increase the volume of work. There should be a gradual approach
to the next schedule which will take a form something like this:

Schedule 2

1) 300 metres gentle swimming of any stroke (warm up).
2) 4 × 200 metres swim using more than one stroke, within
   1½ minutes rest after each 200 metres.
3) 4 × 25 metres legs-only practice, with 30 seconds rest on
   each 25 metres. Leg kicking only should be done with a float
   extended to the front; this is a good conditioner and will
   improve the stroke generally.
4) 200 metres full stroke using the stroke you have just used
   for legs only.
5) Swim down for 5 minutes, using any stroke to relax.

   This schedule will last longer than the first and will again take
some time for the body to adapt to the increase in effort.

   The next stage is to vary the pace of your swims and use all
the stroke skills you know. The theme now should be 'looking
for variation' — and not to get bored! You will be finding a
measure of satisfaction, knowing that your strokes are improving
and that the distances covered are getting greater, with some
improvement in the swimming times. We should be ready now
to attempt a more varied schedule, besides extending our effort.
The next schedule will look something like the following:

Schedule 3

1) 400 to 500 metres warm up.
2) 6 × 50 metres favourite stroke only, 30 seconds rest.
3) 3 × 200 metres using three strokes, one minute rest each
   200 metres.
4) 4 × 50 metres legs only, with the float extended.
5) 4 × 50 metres arms only, with the float between the legs.
6) 4 × 100 metres using the same stroke as used on arms and
   legs practices. 45 seconds rest between each 100 metres.
7) Swim down for 5 minutes and relax.

   This last schedule covers over 2,000 metres, so once you get
this far, there is no stopping you. You might even be thinking
about taking part in a Masters' Swimming Programme.

These schedules are designed to serve as guidelines only. Ideally a schedule should be tailored to your own particular needs and ability. If you find that you are capable of more effort, then by all means develop these suggestions, but if you find these schedules difficult to achieve at first, keep going, work on your strokes and you will soon begin to feel the results.

Swimming and asthma

Asthma sufferers and others with breathing difficulties such as hayfever victims can take heart by knowing that swimming can be one of the safest forms of exercise and one which also improves all-round fitness and confidence. Asthma is a reversible disease, a normal life can be led with the assistance of modern drugs. There are many prescribed drugs available, which prevent the onset of an attack of asthma, such as Becotide or Intal and there are others that can be used when medication is needed during a period of breathlessness.

What we want is a better state of fitness in order to prevent an attack of asthma. The specific advantages of swimming for asthma sufferers are numerous. Exercise in water improves the elasticity of the muscles of the rib cage, giving the intercostal muscles a greater range of movement and thus allowing a greater uptake of oxygen through the lungs. The environment of the swimming pool with its warm moist air is also distinctly beneficial to the asthmatic, being much easier on the lungs than dry air loaded with dust particles. In swimming the ribs have to work harder because of the increased pressure of the water, but the timing of the stroke cycle also assists in breath control. A further advantage of swimming for asthma sufferers is the psychological benefit, something lacking for asthmatics in most other forms of exercises, including running, which *can cause* problems with breathing.

Quite a number of top competitive swimmers are asthmatic, yet they attain world class status and maintain this high standard for many years. So someone with this breathing problem need not sit on the touch line watching others enjoy their sport: they too can 'get in the swim'.

So how would a swim fitness programme for asthmatics differ?

Firstly, as a normal precaution, have whatever medication the doctor has prescribed readily available and, perhaps, use the 'puffer' of Intal, Becotide or other medication before exercise begins. Try to be self-reliant though, and not to depend too much on medication. Be sensible: you can follow the same programme of schedules already mentioned, but moderation should be the key. Work and still look for progress, however, because motivation stems from this.

Exercise which raises the heart rate to say 140 to 160 and lasts for more than five minutes, non-stop, is more likely to cause an asthma attack about five minutes after the exercise has stopped. On the other hand exercise which lasts for shorter durations (that is for two to three minutes at the same level) causes an increase in the width of the air tubes and will increase your breathing capacity over all. Short periods of activity, therefore, are of greater benefit to the asthmatic than prolonged intense sessions of exercise.

Asthma can be lived with, especially with modern medicines and knowledge. Don't think that you are a second class citizen, far from it, but you have got to prove this point and what better way to do it, than in the water!

Ante/post natal swimming

We have now looked at the average able-bodied person who wants to achieve a better state of fitness and also those suffering from asthma, but there are other groups for whom swimming is a particularly appropriate exercise. One of these concerns the physically fit ladies who are temporarily not the same shape as they were some months previously, namely the pregnant mums-to-be.

Swimming is one of the most enjoyable forms of exercise and, as we know, something in which the whole family can take part. You can participate from the earliest age, right through your life. For many years, expectant mums have gone swimming, possibly not fully appreciating the benefits that they were deriving from this activity.

In 1985 the Amateur Swimming Association started organized classes for ante-natal water therapy at the National Sports Centre at Crystal Palace in London. These classes were, and still are conducted by professionally qualified swimming staff with the assistance and acceptance of medical back-up, and similar classes are now found in most large cities.

Ideally, these organized classes should take place in warm water, about 86°F (30°C) with exclusive use, and out of the public gaze. This point must be borne in mind for religious reasons, where ethnic minority groups are attending, but is something appreciated by most pregnant mums. Shallow water is also advisable since exercising in water need not mean you have to be a proficient swimmer, far from it. Maternity swim costumes are not a necessity, particularly if classes are being held in an exclusive pool (mums-to-be can wear panties and bras and perhaps one of dad's tee shirts — most comfortable and inexpensive).

Exercises

What is the difference between land and water exercise during pregnancy? Both, of course, have their place and ideally should run along side each other, although a bonus gained from water exercise is that once in the water no one is aware of your 'bump'. Many mothers-to-be are very conscious of their change in profile and welcome the veil of water around them when exercising.

Especially during latter pregnancy, the buoyancy of the water makes the body weightless and easier to move through individual exercises. Many mothers-to-be are surprised that they do not sink with their added poundage. Working against water pressure requires fewer repetitions of set skills, but still allows muscles to be worked to capacity and through the full range of movement. Because the water lends support to the body, injury to mother or child is less likely than on land. It is preferable that exercise is carried out with the body more or less totally immersed. Mothers-to-be who experience backache during pregnancy find water therapy especially helpful. Exercising in water tones up the whole body, keeps the joints more flexible and the muscles more active during a period when other activities may be more difficult. The heart, lungs and blood supply have to work that little bit harder and provide an overall feeling of well-being. Exercising in water is relaxing and especially kind to mums-to-be in hot weather when heat takes its toll of the pregnant mothers' energy.

When and how often

The mum-to-be should start exercising as early as possible — appropriate exercise can only help the mother to feel as fit as possible during her pregnancy. In fact water exercise can be carried out until the actual birth as long as the mother-to-be is feeling fit and well. Some mothers have been known to commence labour whilst participating in these classes, and that is when medical back up is vital to the safety and confidence of swimmer and teacher.

Medical approval

If you feel water exercise may be for you, it is advisable to consult your doctor or midwife first and get their blessing. Only they have your complete medical history and are in a position to advise. If you have had a previous miscarriage or bleeding during your present pregnancy, it may be advisable not to exercise until things are back to normal. Other points that may prevent you exercising are anaemia, infection, persistent contractions, water breaking, toxaemia, nausea and odema. There is a suggestion that swimming during pregnancy helps to shorten labour but since labour also depends on such things as the size and position of the baby, hormonal balance and emotional state, this is hard to prove. What is clear is that with exercise the mother-to-be can cope better during labour: well-toned muscles stretch for a better delivery and quicker recovery.

Post natal

Having had your baby, you will find your weight will fall off far quicker if you have exercised so try to get back into the pool as quickly as possible to tone up. This will help you to prevent long term problems, such as keeping extra weight, prolapse or varicose veins. Check with your doctor/midwife who will advise when you can return to the water, but a general guide line is when bleeding has stopped. Most classes run ante- and post-natal exercises alongside each other, and this is often the only time the two really meet, because in clinics there are separate classes. Psychologically, it gives a boost to the mums still waiting, to see and talk to the proud mums with their new babies.

It will probably take at least three months to get your figure back. The tummy and thighs, areas where weight can be a problem, need particular attention.

You should not take up water exercises whilst pregnant without medical approval and supervision. Attend a class with qualified and experienced staff who will ensure that the water is the right depth and temperature and that adequate changing facilities exist. For further information on where these classes take place, contact your local swimming pool or the Amateur Swimming Association at Harold Fern House, Derby Square, Loughborough, Leicestershire, LE11 0AL.

Swimming after injury or illness

Swimming can be a great help in restoring or increasing physical fitness after injury or illness. Obviously, the buoyancy of water is of assistance to weakened muscles: the assistance that water provides in supporting the body may allow many more muscular activities to take place than would be the case on land. As with an able-bodied person, the cardio-vascular system is assisted because breathing can be controlled by the stroke cycle, and gentle water pressure on the rib cage provides isometric exercise.

There are, however, certain medical conditions which prevent water activities: individuals with open sores, ear infections, heavy colds or bronchitis or fevers should avoid swimming. On the other hand, sufferers from backache or arthritis find tremendous relief in being immersed in water and doing gentle exercises.

With any leg injury, arms-only practices should be undertaken while an arm out of action can be countered by using a float extended in front, using legs only for conditioning. Once your doctor has advised gentle exercise, ask whether swimming should be considered, and if so, start with an easy schedule adapted from those given earlier as appropriate. Care must be taken with your injury when showering off and drying in a changing room, but it is surprising how quickly one adapts to coping with these problems.

Swim as often as possible, not just once a week, and build up the effort and length of time on each session. Exercise within your limits: no discomfort or pain should be involved at any stage. Many public swimming pools offer organized classes for fitness swimming which include guidance for persons recovering from illness or injury, with a trained coach giving personal attention to the needs of the individual. Feelings of depression that often accompany an illness or injury can also be countered through a swimming programme. If you are feeling depressed through not being fit and well, get out and do something about it, once you have the medical clearance. Many physically handicapped individuals can achieve a great deal in water and their infirmities are less obvious to others than on land.

Masters' swimming — for the older swimmer

Many older swimmers, including a large number who have only recently taken up the sport, have discovered the benefits and fun of competitive swimming. This side of swimming has taken off over the past five years to such an extent that it is now seriously supported all over the world. In America it is big business. There is now a World Masters' Swimming Championship (first held in Tokyo in 1986) and a European Masters' Championship which took place at Blackpool in 1987. Masters' swimming is in five year age bands: 25-29 years; then 30-34 years and so on up to 75 years and over. Particularly in the latter categories a novice swimmer can swim along side a former National Champion and in some cases beat him.

Masters' swimming is for both men and women and is a marvellous way to keep fit, be competitive and meet new friends. Not long ago, any swimmer over 20 years old would not be welcome at a competitive swimming club and would have to train alone amongst recreational swimmers. Now most swimming clubs cater for Masters' swimming training, and arrange galas with older swimmers representing the respective clubs. Here are some further schedules that can be undertaken in your swimming for fitness programme, leading on to competitive Masters' swimming.

Schedule — for not-very-active 40-year-olds (and over)

Stage 1

Two sessions per week.
Swim for 20 minutes, easy stroking gradually increasing the

distance and time covered.
Look for better stroke technique.

Stage 2
Two to three sessions per week.
Use a 4-minute warm up, without stopping. Swim 25 metres on medium pace (favourite stroke), then rest for 45 seconds, repeat this 4 times. Check the clock on each 25 metre swim and record the time.
Swim down and relax for 5 minutes.

Stage 3
Three sessions per week.
Swim a 5-minute warm up, using more than one stroke continuously.
Swim 25 metres, faster pace than before, rest for 45 seconds and repeat 6 times. Check for good times on the clock, trying to hold the time or better each 25 metres.
Swim 2 × 50 metres medium pace. Log the best times. One minute rest between each swim.
Five minutes swim down, using 2 strokes.

Stage 4
Swim 3 times per week.
Warm up for 5 minutes using 3 strokes continuously.
Swim 4 × 100 metres on first stroke, one minute rest between swims, record each 100 metres time.
Swim continuously for 6 minutes and record the distance covered.
Swim 10 × 25 metres, 30 seconds rest each 25 metres. Try to hold the time recorded on the first swim.
Swim down for 5 minutes.

Schedule for under 40-year-olds (and for the fitter over-40s)

Stage 1
Swim 2 to 3 times per week.
Warm up swim for 5 minutes non stop.
Swim 25 metres on best stroke and record the time.

Continuous swim for 3 minutes on 2 strokes.

Swim 4 × 25 metres on your best stroke, try to equal the recorded best time for each 25 metres, 30 seconds rest on each swim.

Swim down for 5 minutes and relax.

Stage 2

Swim 2 to 3 times per week.

Warm up on front crawl for 4 minutes.

Swim 50 metres best stroke and record the time.

Swim 200 metres on second stroke easy swimming.

Swim 4 × 50 metres on best stroke, try to equal the recorded best time for each 50 metres. One minute rest after each 50 metres.

Swim down until relaxed.

Stage 3

Swim 3 times per week.

Warm up on front and back crawl for 5 minutes.

Swim 100 metres best stroke, record the time.

Swim 4 × 25 metres, legs only with float extended.

Swim 4 × 25 metres, arms only, float held between thighs. Take 30 seconds rest after each 25 metres swim.

4 × 50 metres second best stroke, with a 30 seconds rest each 50 metres.

3 × 100 metres best stroke, to equal the best recorded time each 100 metres. One minute rest each 100 metres.

Swim down for 5 minutes.

Stage 4

Swim at least 3 times each week.

Five minute warm up on front stroke, back crawl, alternate 50 metres.

Swim 400 metres straight swim and record the time.

Swim 10 × 25 metres on best stroke, holding the best recorded time. Take a 30 seconds rest after each 25 metres.

4 × 50 metres, legs only, on first stroke.

4 × 50 metres, arms only, on first stroke, 30 seconds rest each 50 metres.

Swim 4 × 50 metres first stroke looking for the best time recorded on each 50. One minute rest after each 50 metres.

Swim 6 × 25 metres alternate first and second strokes with only 15 seconds rest each 25 metres.
Swim down until relaxed.

These schedules can be varied according to how often you swim and how much effort you put into each work-out. Remember to work hard, but not to the extent that undue pain or discomfort is felt. Better a gradual gain in water fitness, than a 'bull at a gate' approach, leaving yourself worse off than when you started.

Some serious Masters' training schedules

1 hour schedule

400 metres warm up on all strokes.
2 × 200 metres first stroke, on technique, one minute rest between.
4 × 50 metres, legs only, 30 seconds rest on each 50 metres.
4 × 50 metres, arms only, 30 seconds rest on each 50 metres.
4 × 100 metres same stroke, one minute rest between.
400 metres swim down.
Total: 2,000 metres

1½ hour schedule

600 metres warm up (choice of stroke).
10 × 100 metres, front/back crawl, every 2½ minutes.
200 metres breast stroke, working on technique.
2 × 100 metres, legs only, one minute rest each 100 metres.
2 × 100 metres, arms only, one minute rest each 100 metres.
2 × 400 metres, front crawl (for endurance) one minute rest.
Swim down to finish.
Total: 3,000 metres plus

1¾ to 2 hour schedule

This is known as a 'Hungarian Rep Session'.
Ten minute warm up swim.
8 × 50 metres, third stroke, every 60 seconds.
4 × 100 metres, second stroke, every 2½ minutes.
2 × 200 metres, first stroke, every 4 minutes.

400 metres straight swim, front crawl.
2 × 200 metres, third stroke, every 4 minutes.
4 × 100 metres, first stroke, every 2 minutes.
8 × 50 metres, second stroke, every 60 seconds.
Total: 3,500 metres plus

Once you have reached a state of fitness which can cope with schedules like this, then there is not much wrong physically or mentally. Remember to build up slowly and allow your body to adapt to the extra stress.

Even a little swimming will do you good, and even if only sections of the earlier schedules can be achieved, you will have some sort of guide to your progress towards greater fitness. The times given for each practice may have to be adjusted initially, to suit your own needs, but try and stick to the targets set.

Some swimming dos and don'ts

Before commencing a fitness for swimming programme, consult your doctor if you have a medical problem, or any doubts. Start slowly and build up, progressively. Muscle aches and pains will appear, but don't be put off. Do not eat for at least one hour before swimming to allow the blood to be used for the digestive system. If you experience any undue, sudden or sharp pain — then stop. Chest pains in particular mean that you should seek medical advice.

Enjoy your swimming programme and try to encourage others to join in with you!

TAKE THE PLUNGE — THE WATER'S GREAT!

Useful Addresses

Amateur Swimming Association,
Harold Fern House,
Derby Square,
Loughborough,
Leics LE11 0AL

The Institute of Swimming Teachers and Coaches Ltd,
38 Leicester Road,
Loughborough,
Leics LE11 2AG

Irish ASA,
6 Maywood Crescent,
Dublin 5,
Eire,
Ireland

Scottish ASA,
Airthrey Castle,
University of Stirling,
Stirling, FK9 4LA
Scotland

Welsh ASA,
National Sports Centre for Wales,
Sophia Gardens,
Cardiff CF1 9SW,
Wales

Aquatic Federation of Canada,
2180 Marine Drive,
Suite 1607,
Oakville,
Ontario,
Canada L6L 5V2

United States Swimming,
1750 E. Boulder St.,
Colorado Springs,
C080909
USA

Australian Swimming Inc.,
PO Box 133,
Chatswood,
NSW 2067,
Australia

New Zealand Amateur Swimming Assoc.,
PO Box 11-115,
Wellington,
New Zealand

Asthma Research Council
300 Upper Street
Islington
London N1 2XX